Music Theory Past Papers 2015

ABRSM Grade 1

Theory Paper   Grade 1   2015   A

Duration 1½ hours

Candidates should answer ALL questions.
Write your answers on this paper – no others will be accepted.
Answers must be written clearly and neatly – otherwise marks may be lost.

TOTAL MARKS
100

1 (a) Add the time signature to each of these three melodies.

10

(b) Add a rest at each of the two places marked * to make the bars complete.

2 Write a two-bar rhythm as an answer to the given rhythm.

10

3 (a) Give the letter name of each of the notes marked ∗, including the flat sign v
   necessary. The first answer is given.

A
....

(b) Draw a circle around two notes next to each other that are a 6th apart.

4 Write the dynamics   *p*   *mf*   *pp*   *f*   *ff*   *mp*   in the correct order,
  from the *loudest* to the *quietest*. The first answer is given.

ff
....

5 Add the correct clef to make each of these named notes, as shown in the first answer.

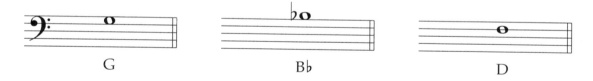

G   Bb   D

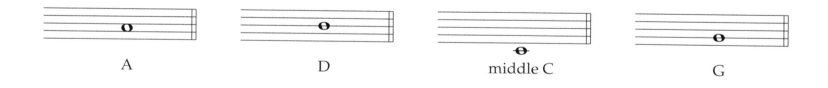

A   D   middle C   G

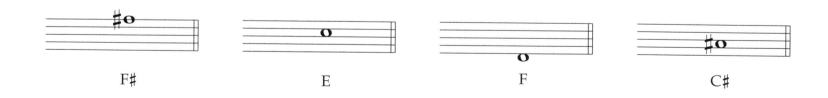

F♯   E   F   C♯

6 Rewrite the following melody, grouping (beaming) the notes correctly.

Marcello (adapted)

7 (a) Draw a circle around the *higher* note of each of these pairs of notes.

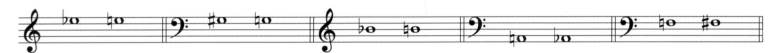

(b) Draw a circle around the *lower* note of each of these pairs of notes.

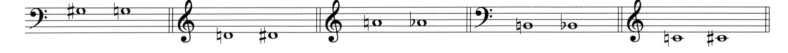

8 Look at this melody, which is adapted from a piece by Liszt, and then answer the questions below.

Write your answer to question (c) on the stave below.

(a) Give the meaning of:

Andante ....

moderato ....

$\boldsymbol{p}$ ....

cantabile ....

 (bar 5) ....

(b) (i) This melody is in the key of D major. Name the degree of
the scale (e.g. 4th, 5th, 6th) of the first note in bar 5 (marked ∗). ....

(ii) Draw a circle around a note in this melody that is *not* in the key of D major.

(iii) Give the time name (e.g. crotchet or
quarter note) of the *shortest* note in the melody. ....

(iv) Complete this sentence:
Bars 1 and 2 have the same notes and rhythm as bars .... and ....

(v) How many bars contain a quaver (eighth-note) rest? ....

(c) Copy out the music from the start of bar 4 to the end of bar 7, exactly as it is written
above. Don't forget the clef, key signature, dynamics and all other details. Write
the music on the blank stave above question (a). (Marks will be given for neatness
and accuracy.)

Theory Paper   Grade 1   2015   B

TOTAL MARKS
100

Duration 1½ hours

Candidates should answer ALL questions.
Write your answers on this paper – no others will be accepted.
Answers must be written clearly and neatly – otherwise marks may be lost.

1   Add the missing bar-lines to these two melodies. The first bar-line is given in each.   [10]

Schumann

Haydn

2   Write a two-bar rhythm as an answer to the given rhythm.   [10]

3   Write as semibreves (whole notes) the scales named below, using the correct key signature for each.   [10]

G major, descending

F major, ascending

4 Add a rest at the places marked ∗ in these two melodies to make each bar complete.   10

5 (a) Name the degree of the scale (e.g. 2nd, 3rd, 4th) of each of the notes marked ∗, as shown in the first answer. The key is C major.   10

2nd

....

(b) How many times does middle C occur in this melody? ....

6 (a) Add the correct clef to each of these tonic triads.   10

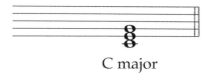

C major

G major

Letter names   ....

(b) Under each triad write the letter name of each note.

7 Give the number (e.g. 2nd, 3rd, 4th) of each of these harmonic intervals, as shown in the first answer. The key is D major.   10

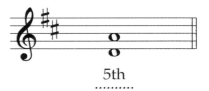

5th
....

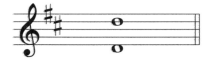

....

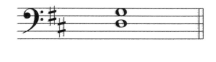

....

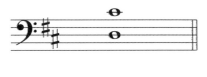

....

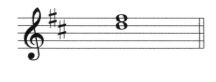

....

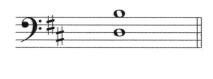

....

8 Look at this folksong melody and then answer the questions below.

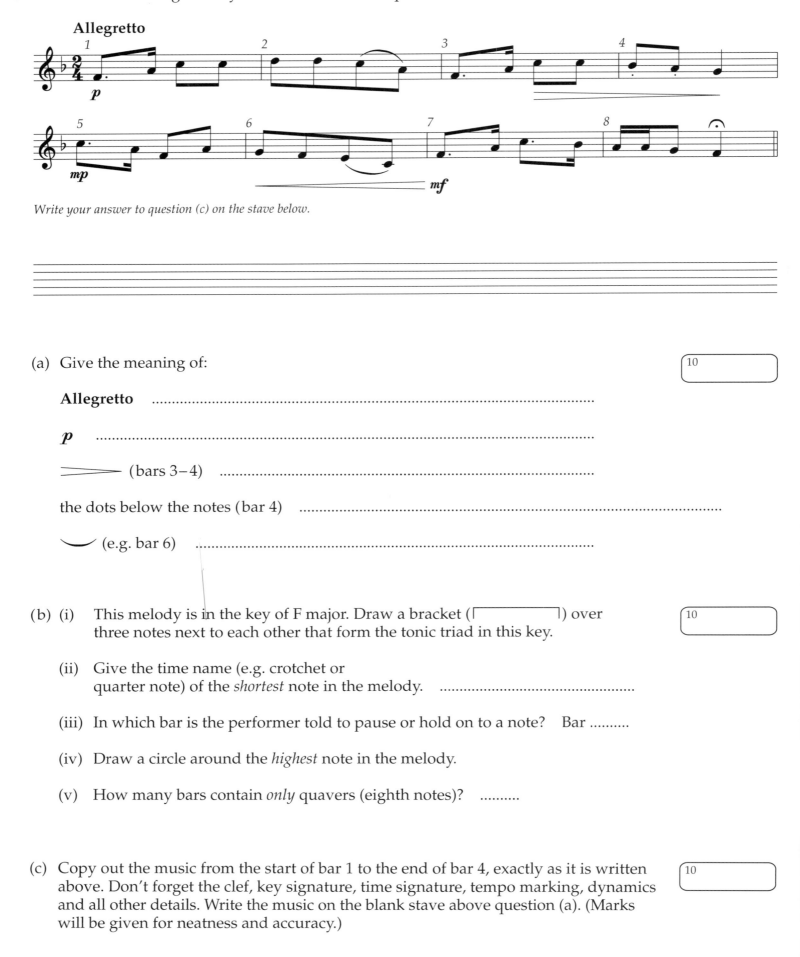

Write your answer to question (c) on the stave below.

(a) Give the meaning of:

Allegretto ....

p ....

⸻ (bars 3–4) ....

the dots below the notes (bar 4) ....

⌣ (e.g. bar 6) ....

(b) (i) This melody is in the key of F major. Draw a bracket (⌐‾‾‾‾‾‾¬) over three notes next to each other that form the tonic triad in this key.

(ii) Give the time name (e.g. crotchet or quarter note) of the *shortest* note in the melody. ....

(iii) In which bar is the performer told to pause or hold on to a note? Bar ....

(iv) Draw a circle around the *highest* note in the melody.

(v) How many bars contain *only* quavers (eighth notes)? ....

(c) Copy out the music from the start of bar 1 to the end of bar 4, exactly as it is written above. Don't forget the clef, key signature, time signature, tempo marking, dynamics and all other details. Write the music on the blank stave above question (a). (Marks will be given for neatness and accuracy.)

10

10

10

Theory Paper   Grade 1   2015   C

Duration 1½ hours

Candidates should answer ALL questions.
Write your answers on this paper – no others will be accepted.
Answers must be written clearly and neatly – otherwise marks may be lost.

TOTAL MARKS
100

1 Add the missing bar-lines to these two melodies. The first bar-line is given in each.

10

Verdi

Mendelssohn

2 Write a two-bar rhythm as an answer to the given rhythm.

10

3 *After* each note write a *higher* note to form the named *melodic* interval, as shown in the first answer. The key is C major.

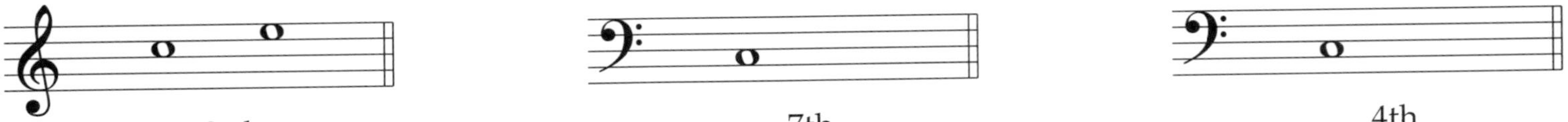

3rd   7th   4th

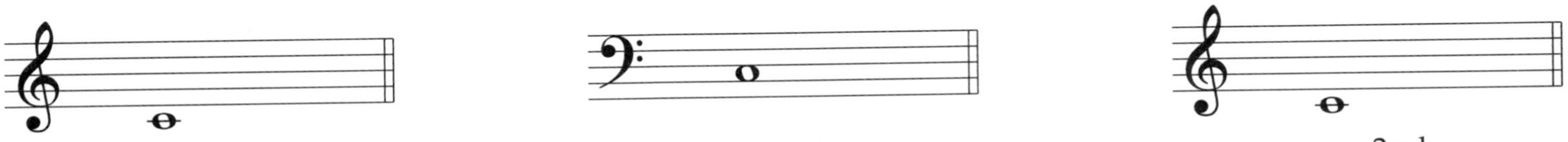

8th/8ve   6th   2nd

4 Name the major keys shown by these key signatures. The first answer is given.

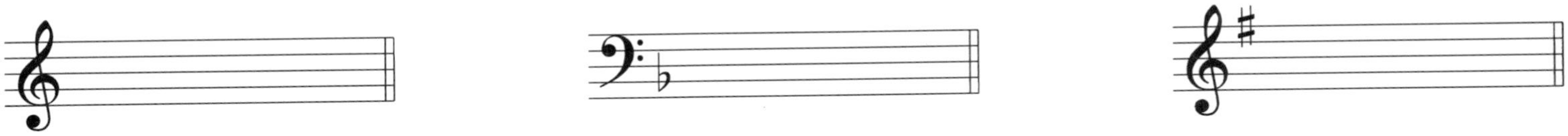

C major

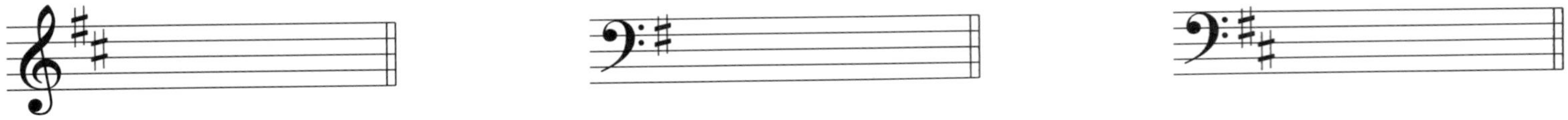

5 (a) Give the letter name of each of the notes marked *, including the sharp sign where necessary. The first answer is given.

Mozart (adapted)

G

(b) Give the time name (e.g. crotchet or quarter note) of the *longest* note in the melody.

....

6 Next to each rest write a note that has the same time value, as shown in the first answer.

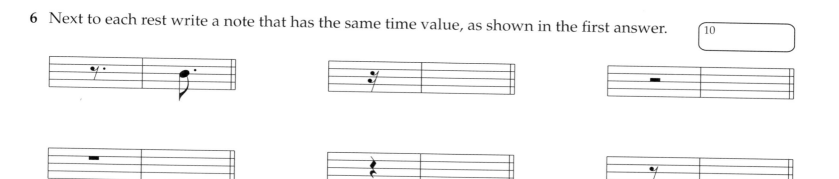

7 Add the correct clef and any necessary sharp or flat signs to make each of the scales named below. Do *not* use key signatures.

D major

F major

8 Look at this melody, adapted from a piece by Sullivan, and then answer the questions below.

Write your answer to question (c) on the stave below.

(a) Give the meaning of:

Allegro ....

♩ = 124 ....

mp ....

cresc. (bar 4) ....

f (bar 5) ....

(b) (i) The melody is in the key of F major. Give the number of a
    bar that contains all the notes of the tonic triad in this key.   Bar ....

    (ii) Name the degree of the scale (e.g. 2nd, 3rd, 4th) of the
    first note of the melody. Remember that the key is F major.   ....

    (iii) Complete this sentence:
    Bar 1 has the same notes and rhythm as bar ....

    (iv) Answer TRUE or FALSE to this sentence:
    The lower **4** in **4/4** means crotchet (quarter-note) beats.   ....

    (v) How many quavers (eighth notes) is the note in bar 4 worth?   ....

(c) Copy out the music from the start of bar 1 to the end of bar 4, exactly as it is written
    above. Don't forget the clef, key signature, time signature, tempo marking, dynamics
    and all other details. Write the music on the blank stave above question (a).
    (Marks will be given for neatness and accuracy.)

Theory Paper   Grade 1   2015   S

TOTAL MARKS
100

Duration 1½ hours

Candidates should answer ALL questions.
Write your answers on this paper – no others will be accepted.
Answers must be written clearly and neatly – otherwise marks may be lost.

1 (a) Add the time signature to each of these three melodies.

10

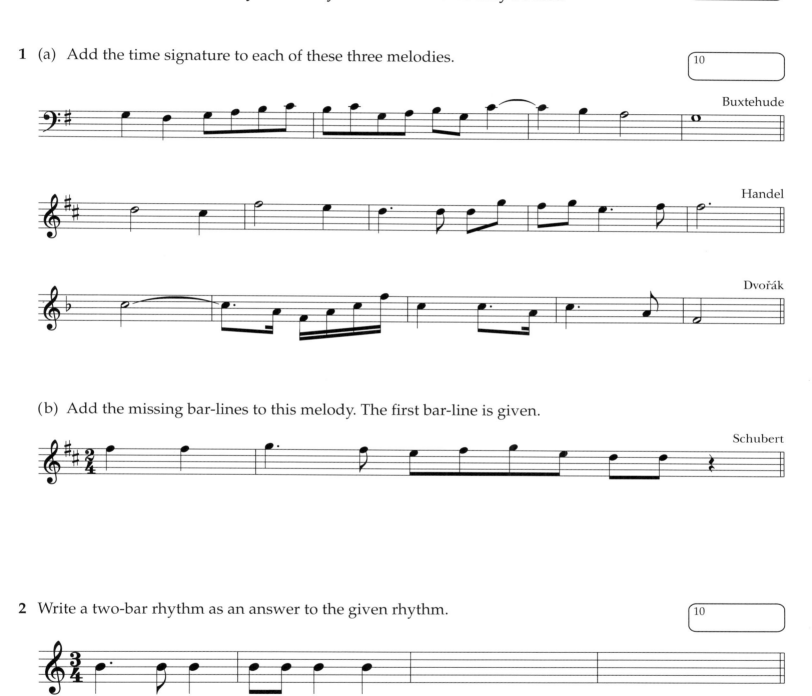

(b) Add the missing bar-lines to this melody. The first bar-line is given.

2 Write a two-bar rhythm as an answer to the given rhythm.

10

3 Add the correct clef and any necessary sharp or flat signs to make each of the scales named below. Do *not* use key signatures.

F major

D major

4 (a) Give the letter name of each of the notes marked ✱, including the sharp sign where necessary. The first answer is given.

Stanford (adapted)

D
....

(b) Give the time name (e.g. crotchet or quarter note) of the *shortest* note in the melody.

....

5 Add a rest at the places marked ✱ to make each bar complete.

Smetana

6 Give the number (e.g. 2nd, 3rd, 4th) of each of these melodic intervals, as shown in the first answer. The key is C major.

.....7th.....

....

....

....

....

....

7 Name the major key of each of these tonic triads, as shown in the first answer.

.....C major.....

....

....

....

....

....

8 Look at this melody by Sullivan and then answer the questions below.

Write your answer to question (c) on the stave below.

(a) Give the meaning of: `10`

Allegretto ....

moderato ....

♩ = 112 ....

mf ....

rall. (bar 6) ....

(b) (i) Complete this sentence: `10`

Bars 1 and 2 have the same notes and rhythm as bars .... and ....

(ii) Give the letter name of the *highest* note in the melody. ....

(iii) Underline one of the following words that best describes how you think bar 3 should
be played: *legato* (smoothly)   or   *staccato* (detached)

(iv) How many quavers (eighth notes) is the note in bar 8 worth? ....

(v) Answer TRUE or FALSE to this sentence:
The upper **4** in **4/4** means the number of beats in a bar. ....

(c) Copy out the music from the start of bar 1 to the end of bar 3, exactly as it is   `10`
written above. Don't forget the clef, key signature, time signature, tempo marking,
dynamic and all other details. Write the music on the blank stave above question (a).
(Marks will be given for neatness and accuracy.)

ABRSM
24 Portland Place
London W1B 1LU
United Kingdom

www.abrsm.org

MIX
Paper from
responsible sources
FSC
www.fsc.org   FSC™ C109619

Published by ABRSM (Publishing) Ltd,
a wholly owned subsidiary of ABRSM
Cover by Kate Benjamin & Andy Potts
Printed in England by Halstan & Co. Ltd,
Amersham, Bucks

ISBN 978-1-84849-755-9

9 781848 497559